The Forties

for Keyboard

arranged and processed by Barnes Music Engraving Ltd
East Sussex TN22 4HA, UK

Cover design by xheight Limited

Published 1995

International
MUSIC
Publications

International Music Publications Limited
Griffin House 161 Hammersmith Road London W6 8BS England

Almost Like Being In Love

Words by Alan Jay Lerner / Music by Frederick Loewe

Suggested Registration: Jazz Guitar
Rhythm: Swing
Tempo: ♩ = 132

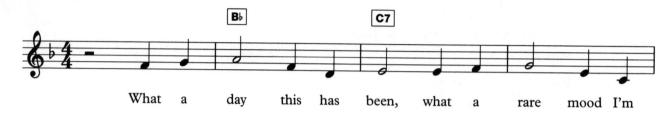

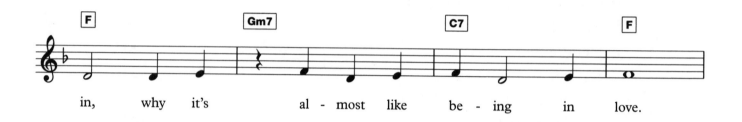

What a day this has been, what a rare mood I'm

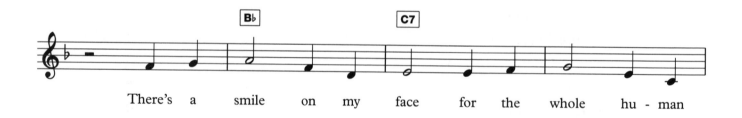

in, why it's al - most like be - ing in love.

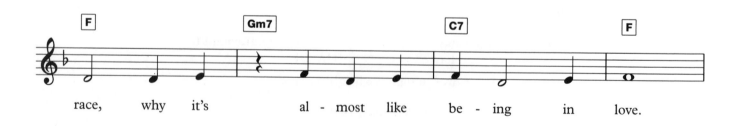

There's a smile on my face for the whole hu - man

race, why it's al - most like be - ing in love.

All the mu - sic of life seems to be

Sam Fox Publishing Co (London) Ltd, London WC2H 0EA

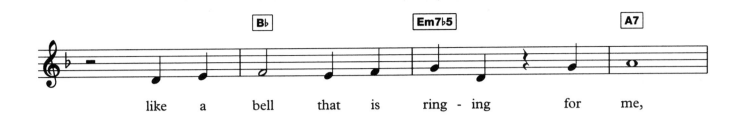

like a bell that is ring - ing for me,

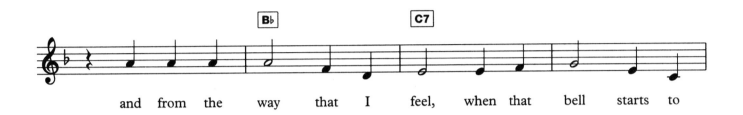

and from the way that I feel, when that bell starts to

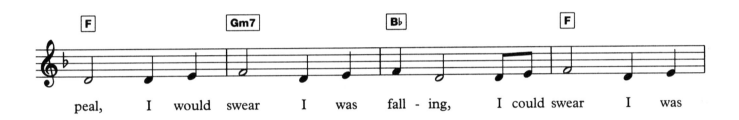

peal, I would swear I was fall - ing, I could swear I was

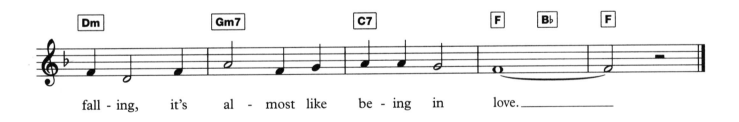

fall - ing, it's al - most like be - ing in love. _____

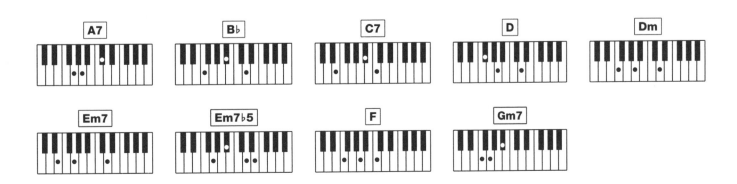

ANOTHER OPENIN', ANOTHER SHOW

Words and Music by Cole Porter

Suggested Registration: Clarinet
Rhythm: March
Tempo: ♩ = 126

An - oth - er op - 'nin', an - oth - er show,__ in

Phil - ly, Bos - ton or Bal - ti - moe,__ a chance for stage - folks to

say, 'Hel - lo,'__ an - oth - er op - 'nin' of an - oth - er show. An -

-oth - er job__ that you hope at last__ will make your fu - ture for -

-get your past,__ an - oth - er pain__ where the ul - cers grow,__ an -

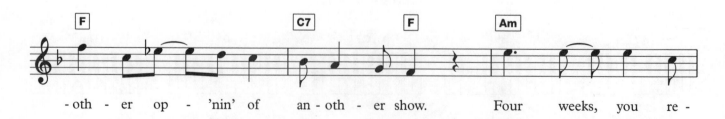

-oth - er op - 'nin' of an - oth - er show. Four weeks, you re -

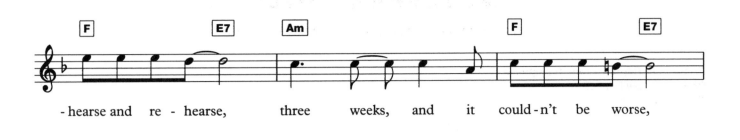

-hearse and re - hearse,   three   weeks,   and   it   could - n't   be   worse,

one   week,_   will   it   ev - er   be   right?_   Then   out o' the hat__   it's   that

big   first   night.   The   o - ver - ture__   is   a - bout   to   start,_   you

cross   your   fin - gers,   and   hold   your   heart,   it's   cur - tain time__   and   a -

- way   we   go,___   an - oth - er   op - 'nin' of   an - oth - er   show.

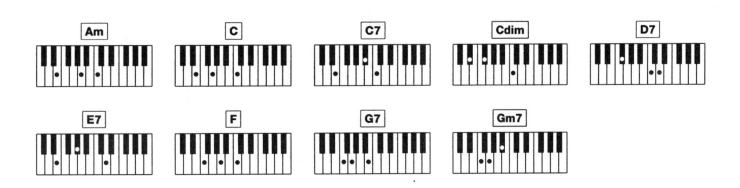

BLUEBERRY HILL

Words and Music by Al Lewis, Larry Stock and Vincent Rose

Suggested Registration: Saxophone
Rhythm: Slow Rock (Swing)
Tempo: ♩ = 108

I found my

thrill ___ on Blue-ber-ry Hill, ___ on Blue-ber-ry Hill,

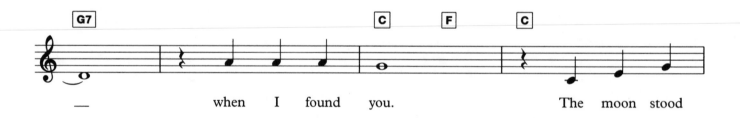

___ when I found you. The moon stood

still ___ on Blue-ber-ry Hill, ___ and ling-ered un-til ___

___ my dreams came true. The wind in the

wil - low played love's sweet me - lo - dy, but all of those

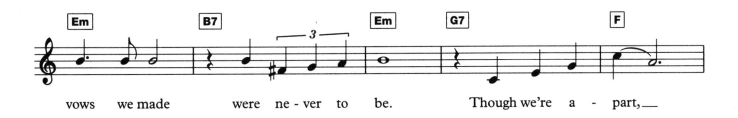

vows we made were ne - ver to be. Though we're a - part,___

you're part of me still,___ for you were my thrill

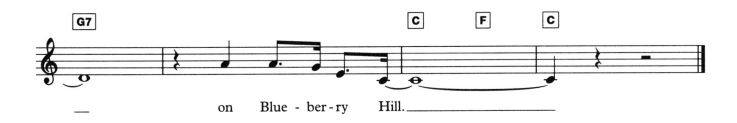

___ on Blue - ber - ry Hill._____

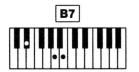
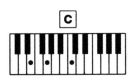
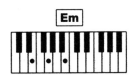
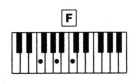

Busy Doin' Nothing

Words by Johnny Burke / Music by James Van Heusen

Suggested Registration: Oboe
Rhythm: March 6/8
Tempo: ♩ = 98

Don't Get Around Much Any More

Words by Bob Russell / Music by Duke Ellington

Suggested Registration: Vibraphone
Rhythm: Swing
Tempo: ♩ = 104

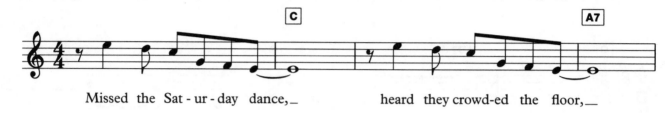

Missed the Sat - ur - day dance, _ heard they crowd-ed the floor, _

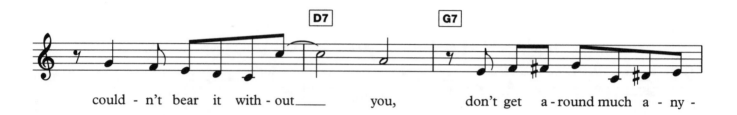

could - n't bear it with - out _ you, don't get a - round much a - ny -

- more. Thought I'd vi - sit the club, _ got as far as the door,

_ they'd have asked me a - bout _ you,

don't get a - round much a - ny - more. _

Dar - ling I guess _ my mind's more at ease, _ but

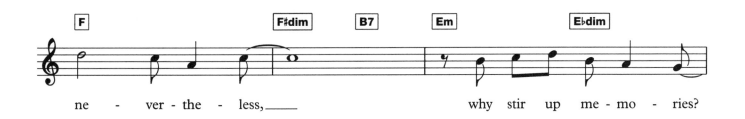

ne - ver - the - less,_____ why stir up me - mo - ries?

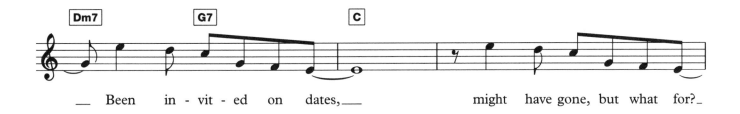

_ Been in - vit - ed on dates,___ might have gone, but what for?_

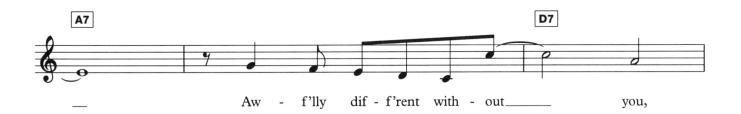

_ Aw - f'lly dif - f'rent with - out_____ you,

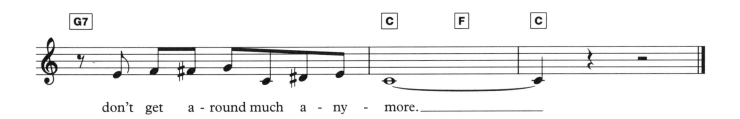

don't get a - round much a - ny - more._____

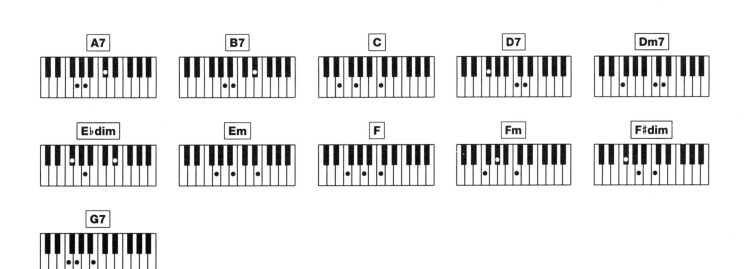

How High The Moon

Words by Nancy Hamilton / Music by Morgan Lewis

Suggested Registration: Strings
Rhythm: Slow Swing
Tempo: ♩ = 88

Some - where there's mu - sic, how faint the tune,

some - where there's hea - ven, how high the moon.

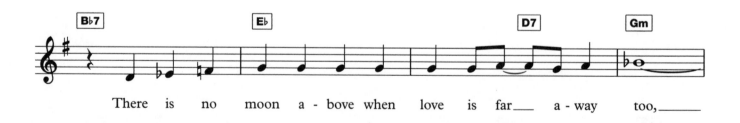

There is no moon a - bove when love is far___ a - way too,___

___ till it comes true, that you love me, and I love

you. Some - where there's mu - sic, it's where you are,

some - where there's hea - ven, how near, how far.

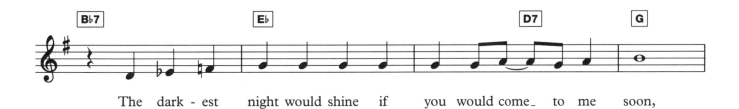

The dark - est night would shine if you would come_ to me soon,

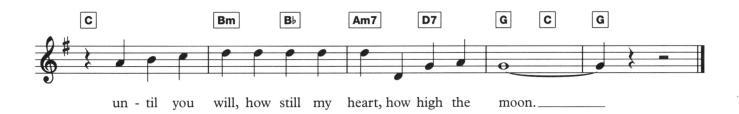

un - til you will, how still my heart, how high the moon._____

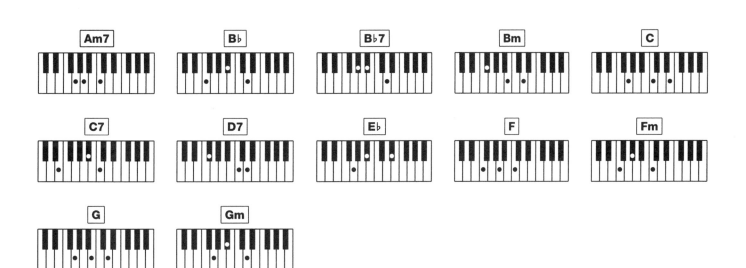

I Don't Want To Set The World On Fire

Words and Music by Eddie Seiler, Sol Marcus, Bennie Benjamin and Eddie Durham

Suggested Registration: Vibraphone
Rhythm: Swing
Tempo: ♩ = 100

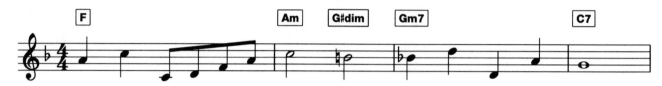

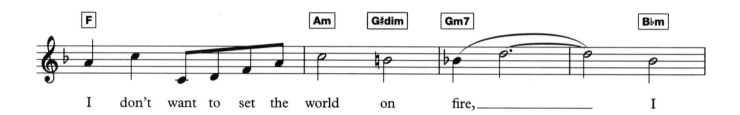

I don't want to set the world on fire, _____ I

just want to start __ a flame in your heart. _____

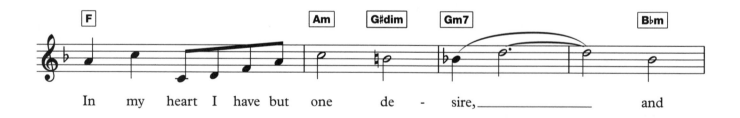

In my heart I have but one de - sire, _____ and

that one is you, __ no - oth - er will do. _____ I've

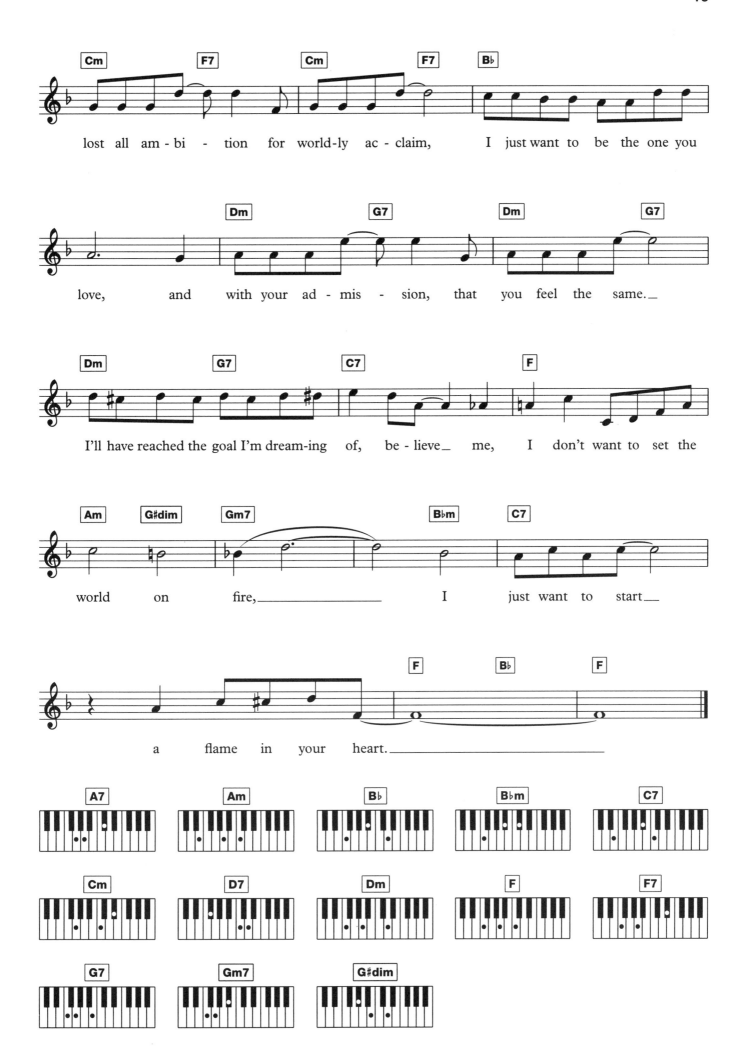

(I Love You) For Sentimental Reasons

Words by Derek Watson / Music by William Best

Suggested Registration: Strings
Rhythm: Soft Rock
Tempo: ♩ = 84

I love you

— for sen - ti - men - tal rea - sons, _____ I hope you do be -

- lieve me, _____ I'll give you my heart. _____

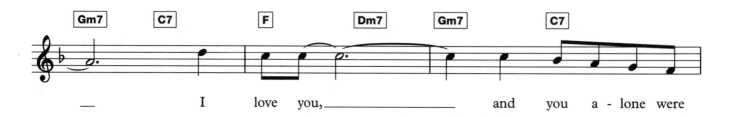

— I love you, _____ and you a - lone were

meant for me, _____ please give your lov - ing heart to me, _____

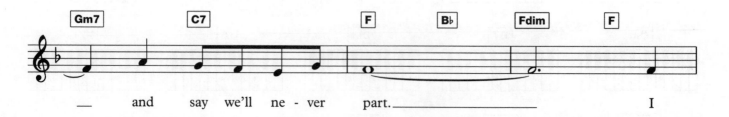

— and say we'll ne - ver part. _____ I

Peter Maurice Music Co Ltd, London WC2H 0EA

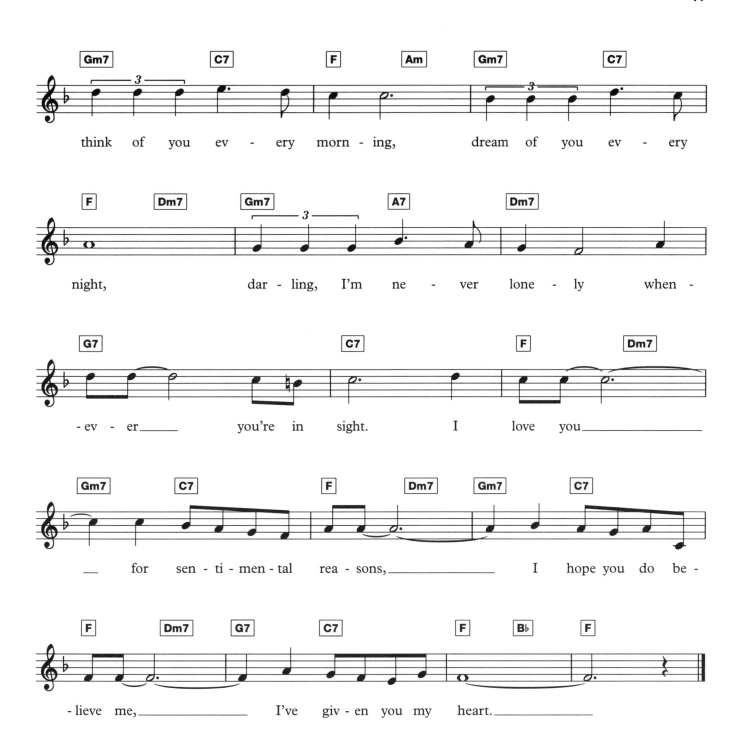

think of you ev - ery morn - ing, dream of you ev - ery

night, dar - ling, I'm ne - ver lone - ly when -

- ev - er____ you're in sight. I love you_____

____ for sen - ti - men - tal rea - sons,_____ I hope you do be -

- lieve me,_____ I've giv - en you my heart._____

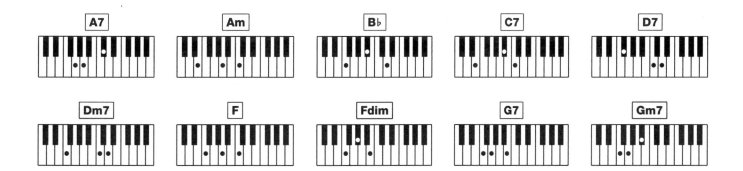

I Remember You

Words by Johnny Mercer / Music by Victor Schertzinger

Suggested Registration: Flute
Rhythm: Slow Swing
Tempo: ♩ = 98

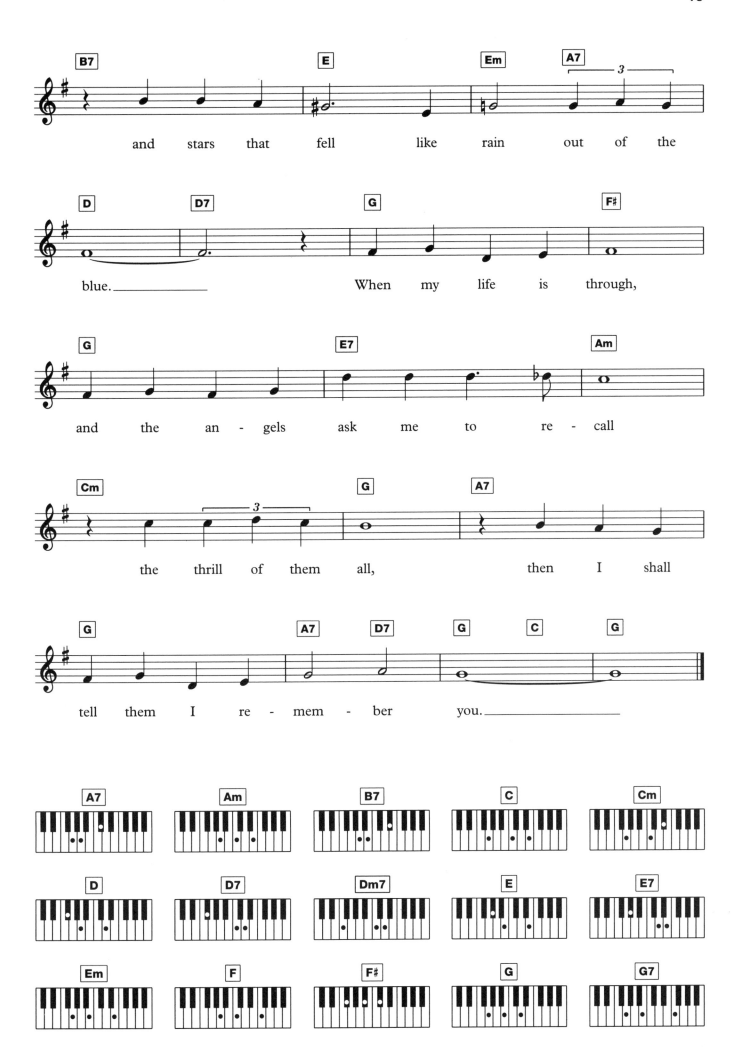

Let There Be Love

Words by Ian Grant / Music by Lionel Rand

Suggested Registration: Piano
Rhythm: Swing
Tempo: ♩ = 108

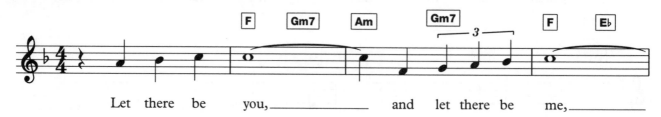

Let there be you,_____ and let there be me,_____

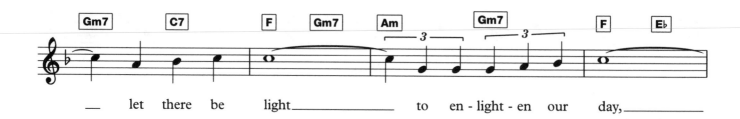

_ let there be moon - light_____ o - ver the sea,_____

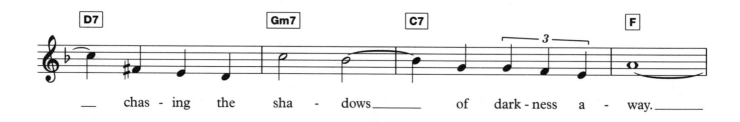

_ let there be light_____ to en - light - en our day,_____

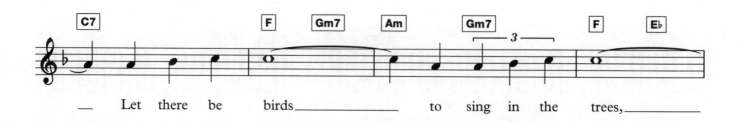

_ chas - ing the sha - dows_____ of dark - ness a - way._____

_ Let there be birds_____ to sing in the trees,_____

some - one to bless me_____ when - ev - er I sneeze,_____

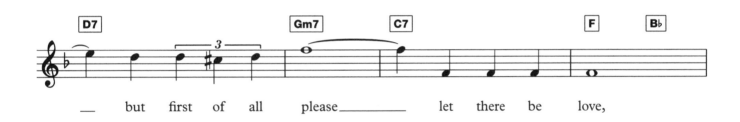

__ let there be cuc - koos,_____ a lark and a dove,_____

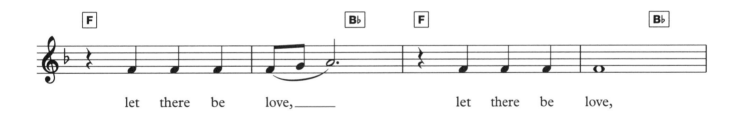

__ but first of all please_____ let there be love,

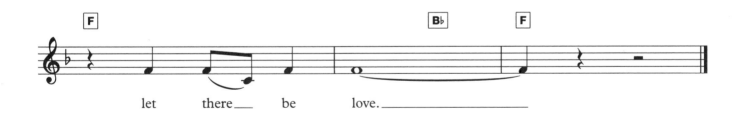

let there be love,_____ let there be love,

let there__ be love._____

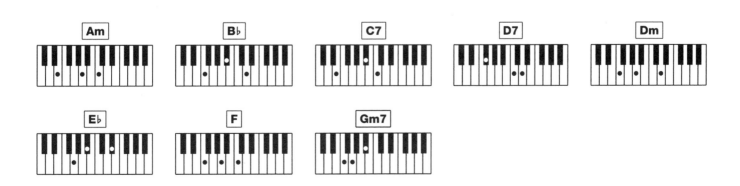

LONG AGO AND FAR AWAY

Words by Ira Gershwin / Music by Jerome Kern

Suggested Registration: Vibraphone
Rhythm: Swing
Tempo: ♩ = 98

Long a - go and far a - way, I
dreamed a dream one day, and now that
dream is here be - side me. Long the
skies were o - ver - cast, but now the clouds have
passed, you're here at last._____

Maybe It's Because I'm A Londoner

Words and Music by Hubert Gregg

Suggested Registration: Saxophone
Rhythm: Slow Swing
Tempo: ♩ = 86

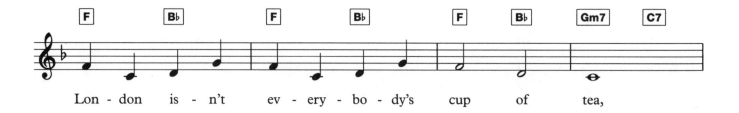

London isn't ev-ery-bo-dy's cup of tea,

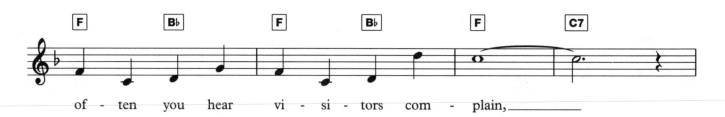

of-ten you hear vi-si-tors com-plain,_____

noi-sy, smo-key ci-ty, but it seems to me

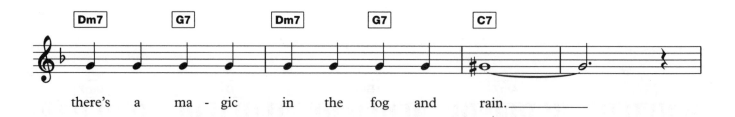

there's a ma-gic in the fog and rain._____

May-be it's be-cause I'm a Lon-don-er,_____ that I love Lon-don so.

May-be it's be-cause I'm a Lon-don-er, that I think of her___ where-ev-er I

go.   I get a fun-ny feel-ing in - side of me_____ just

walk - ing   up   and   down,   may - be   it's   be - cause   I'm   a

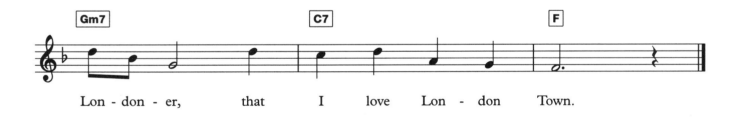

Lon - don - er,   that   I   love   Lon - don   Town.

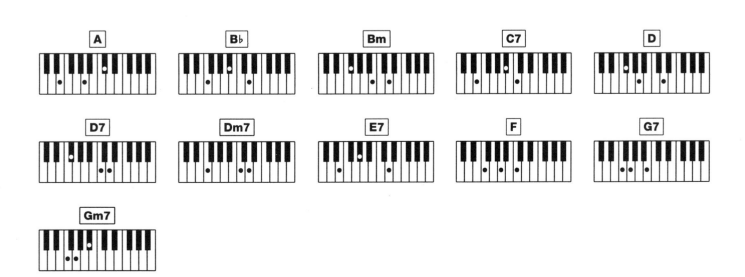

My Foolish Heart

Words by Ned Washington / Music by Victor Young

Suggested Registration: Vibraphone
Rhythm: Soft Rock
Tempo: ♩ = 86

The

night_____ is like a love - ly tune, be - ware_____ my fool - ish

heart, how white_____ the ev - er con - stant moon, take

care_____ my fool - ish heart. There's a line be - tween love and fas - ci -

- na - tion,____ that's hard to see on an eve - ning such as this, for they

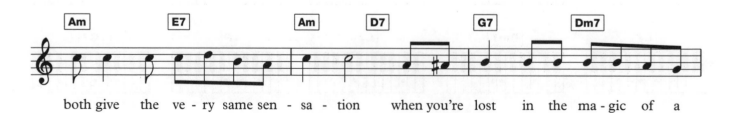

both give the ve - ry same sen - sa - tion when you're lost in the ma - gic of a

The Nearness Of You

Words by Ned Washington / Music by Hoagy Carmichael

Suggested Registration: Electric Piano
Rhythm: Soft Rock
Tempo: ♩ = 92

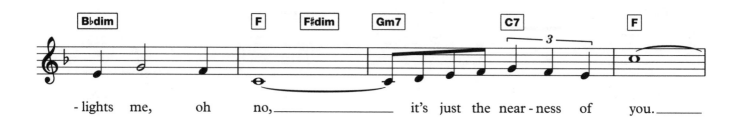

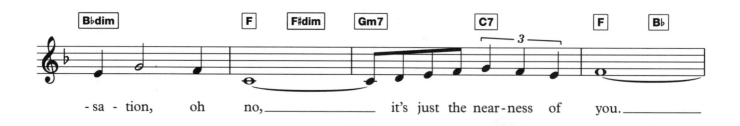

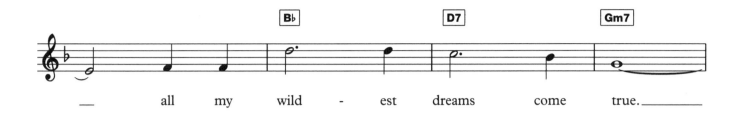

all my wild - est dreams come true.

I need no soft lights to en - chant me, if you'll on - ly

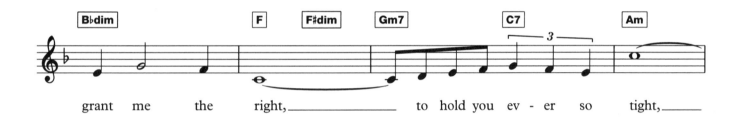

grant me the right, to hold you ev - er so tight,

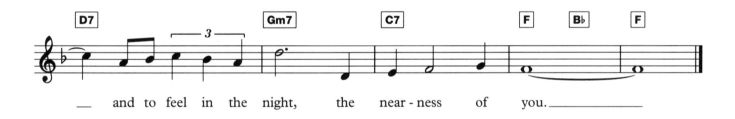

and to feel in the night, the near - ness of you.

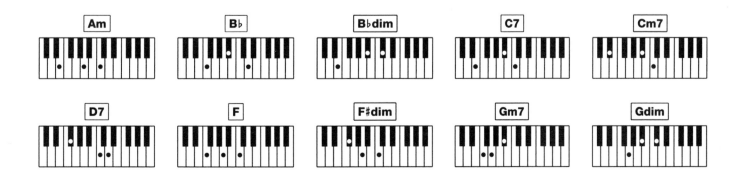

SENTIMENTAL JOURNEY

Words and Music by Bud Green, Les Brown and Ben Homer

Suggested Registration: Clarinet
Rhythm: Slow Swing
Tempo: ♩ = 84

Gon - na take a sen - ti - men - tal jour - ney, gon - na set my

heart at ease, ___ gon - na make a sen - ti - men - tal jour - ney,

to re - new old me - mo - ries. ___ Got my bag, I

got my re - ser - va - tion, spent each dime I could af - ford, ___

like a child in wild an - ti - ci - pa - tion, long to hear that

Stella By Starlight

Words by Ned Washington / Music by Victor Young

Suggested Registration: Accordian
Rhythm: Slow Swing
Tempo: ♩ = 100

The

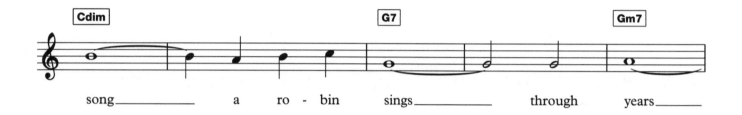

song_____ a ro - bin sings_____ through years_____

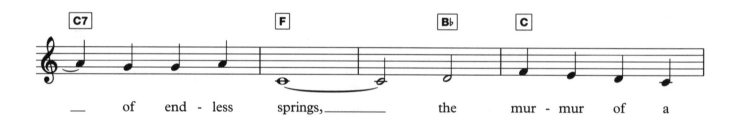

___ of end - less springs,_____ the mur - mur of a

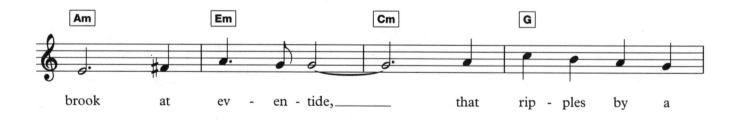

brook at ev - en - tide,_____ that rip - ples by a

nook_____ where two lov - ers hide,_____ a great_____

Swinging On A Star

Words by Johnny Burke / Music by Jimmy Van Heusen

Suggested Registration: Vibraphone
Rhythm: Swing
Tempo: ♩ = 112

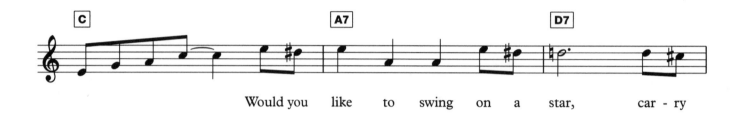

Would you like to swing on a star, car - ry

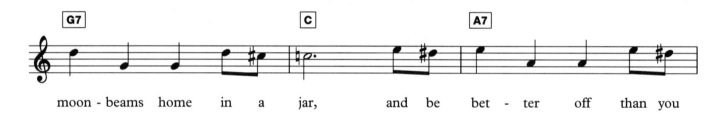

moon - beams home in a jar, and be bet - ter off than you

are, or would you ra - ther be a mule? A

mule is an a - ni - mal with long, fun - ny ears, he kicks up at a - ny-thing he

hears. His back is braw - ny, but his brain is weak, he's

Taking A Chance On Love

Words by John Latouche and Ted Fetter / Music by Vernon Duke

Suggested Registration: Vibraphone
Rhythm: Swing
Tempo: ♩ = 104

Here I go a - gain,_ I hear those trum - pets blow a - gain,_

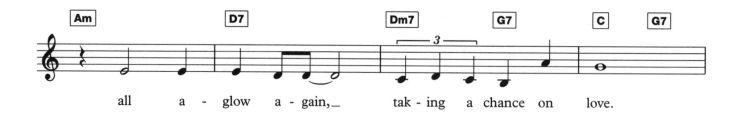

all a - glow a - gain,_ tak - ing a chance on love.

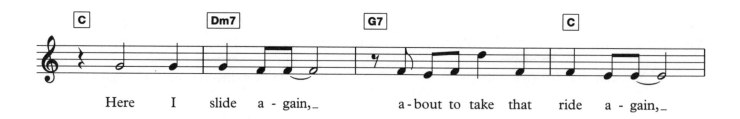

Here I slide a - gain,_ a - bout to take that ride a - gain,_

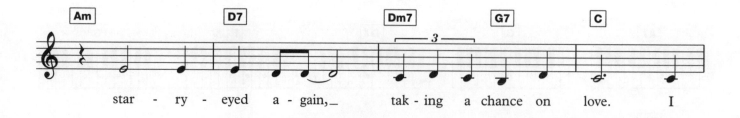

star - ry - eyed a - gain,_ tak - ing a chance on love. I

thought that cards were a frame - up___ I ne - ver___ would try, but

now I'm tak - ing the game up,___ and the ace of hearts is high.

Things are mend - ing now,_ I see a rain - bow blend - ing now,_

we'll have our hap - py end - ing now,_ tak - ing a chance on love.

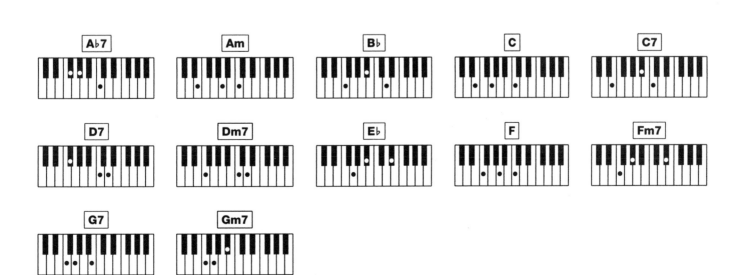

Tenderly

Words by Jack Lawrence / Music by Walter Gross

Suggested Registration: Strings
Rhythm: Waltz
Tempo: ♩ = 84

The eve - ning breeze ca - ressed the trees ten - der - ly.____

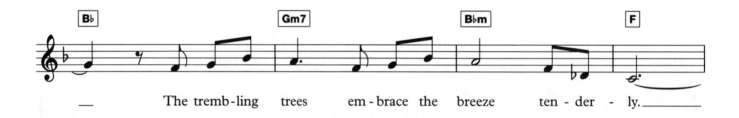

____ The tremb - ling trees em - brace the breeze ten - der - ly.____

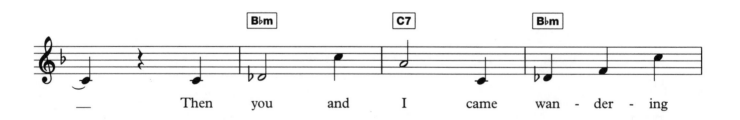

____ Then you and I came wan - der - ing

by, and lost in a sigh were we.____

Warner Chappell Music Ltd, London W1Y 3FA

The shore was kissed by sea and mist ten - der - ly._____

I can't for - get how two hearts met breath-less - ly._____

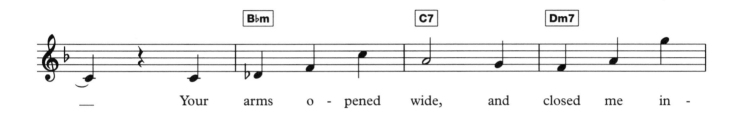

Your arms o - pened wide, and closed me in -

- side, you took my lips, you took my love so ten-der - ly._____

THE TROLLEY SONG

Words and Music by Hugh Martin and Ralph Blane

Suggested Registration: Clarinet
Rhythm: March
Tempo: ♩ = 100

'Clang, clang, clang,' went the trol-ley,___ 'Ding, ding, ding,' went the bell,

'Zing, zing, zing,' went my heart-strings, for the mo-ment I saw him, I fell.

'Chug, chug, chug,' went the mo-tor,___ 'Bump, bump, bump,' went the brake,

'Thump, thump, thump,' went my heart-strings, when he smiled, I could feel the car

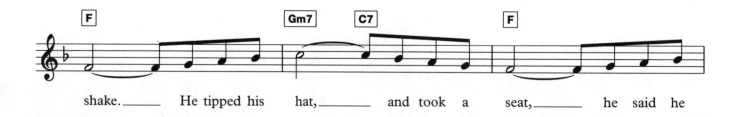

shake.___ He tipped his hat,___ and took a seat,___ he said he

hoped he had-n't stepped up-on my feet,___ he asked my name,___ I held my

The White Cliffs Of Dover

Words by Nat Burton / Music by Walter Kent

Suggested Registration: Flute
Rhythm: Slow Swing
Tempo: ♩ = 104

There'll be

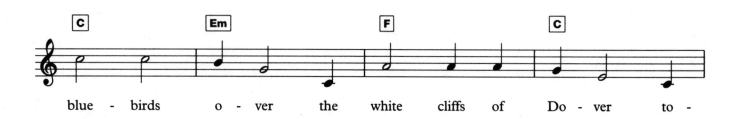

blue - birds o - ver the white cliffs of Do - ver to -

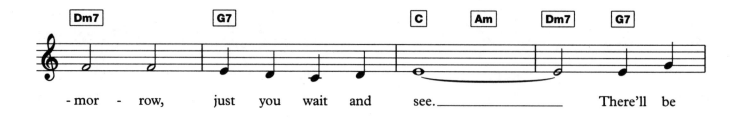

- mor - row, just you wait and see._____ There'll be

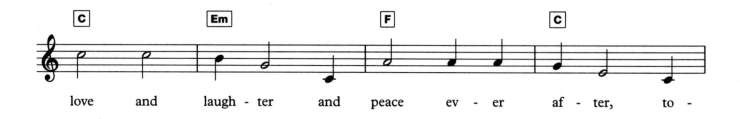

love and laugh - ter and peace ev - er af - ter, to -

- mor - row, when the world is free._____ The

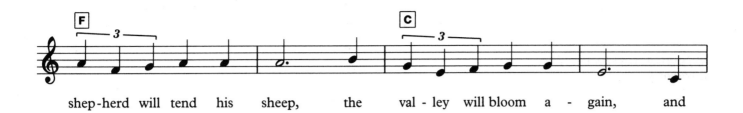

shep-herd will tend his sheep, the val - ley will bloom a - gain, and

Jim - my will go to sleep in his own lit - tle room a - gain. There'll be

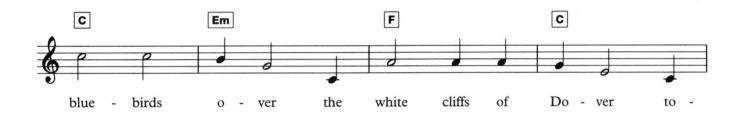

blue - birds o - ver the white cliffs of Do - ver to -

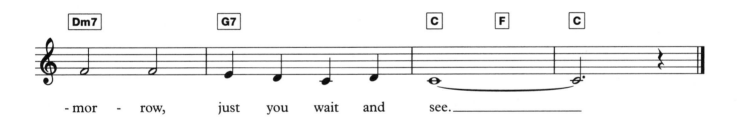

- mor - row, just you wait and see._____

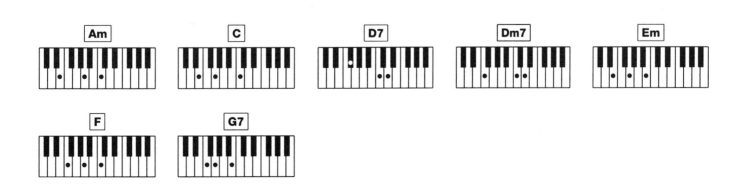

You Make Me Feel So Young

Words by Mack Gordon / Music by Josef Myrow

Suggested Registration: Strings
Rhythm: Swing
Tempo: ♩ = 104

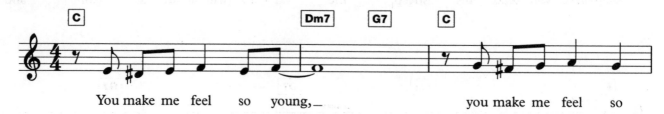

You make me feel so young,— you make me feel so

Spring has sprung, and ev-ery time I see you grin,— I'm such

— a hap-py in-di-vi-du-al. The mo-ment that you speak,—

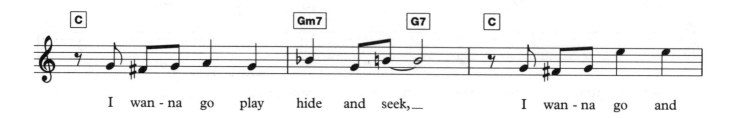

I wan-na go play hide and seek,— I wan-na go and

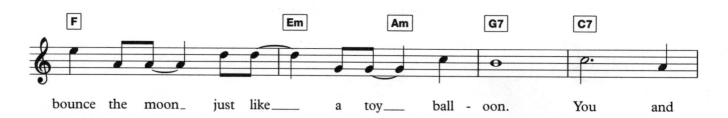

bounce the moon_ just like___ a toy___ ball-oon. You and

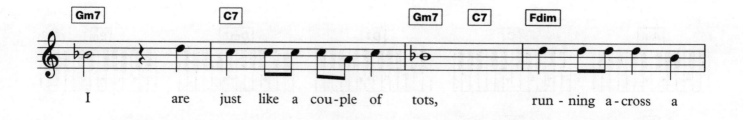

I are just like a cou-ple of tots, run-ning a-cross a

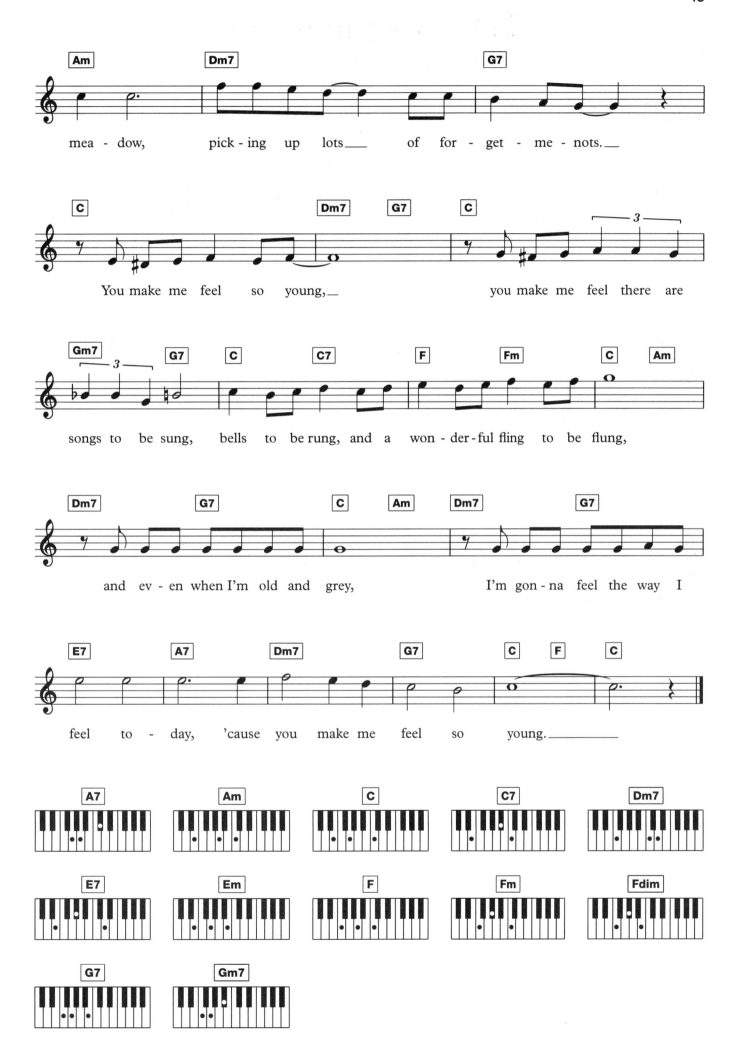

ZIP-A-DEE-DOO-DAH

Words by Ray Gilbert / Music by Allie Wrubel

Suggested Registration: Accordian
Rhythm: March
Tempo: ♩ = 100

Zip - a - dee - doo - dah, zip - a - dee - ay,_____

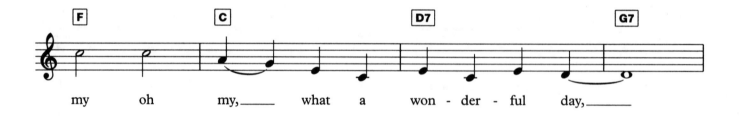

my oh my,_____ what a won - der - ful day,_____

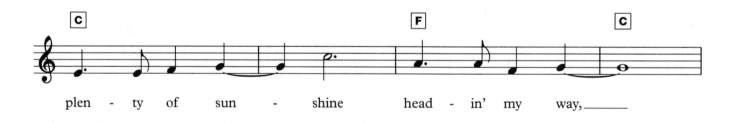

plen - ty of sun - shine head - in' my way,_____

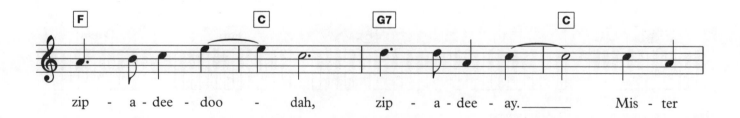

zip - a - dee - doo - dah, zip - a - dee - ay._____ Mis - ter

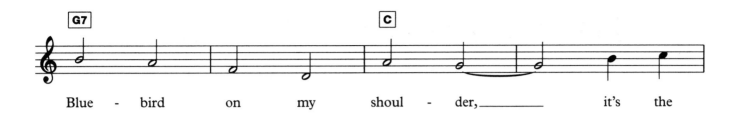

Blue - bird on my shoul - der,_____ it's the

truth, it's 'act - ch'll', ev - ery-thing is 'sa - tis - fact - ch'll'.

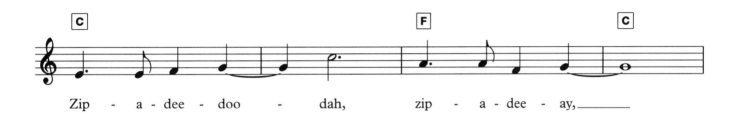

Zip - a - dee - doo - dah, zip - a - dee - ay,_____

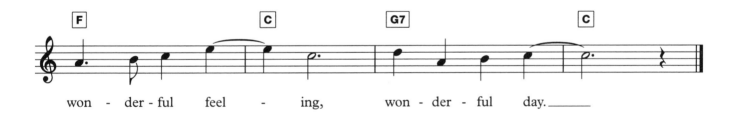

won - der - ful feel - ing, won - der - ful day._____

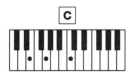

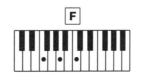

The Easy Keyboard Library Series

Big Band Hits Order Ref: 19098	**Popular Classics** Order Ref: 4180A
Blues Order Ref: 3477A	**Pub Singalong Collection** Order Ref: 3954A
Celebration Songs Order Ref: 3478A	**Rock 'n' Roll Classics** Order Ref: 2224A
Christmas Carols Order Ref: 4616A	**Traditional Scottish Favourites** Order Ref: 4231A
Christmas Songs Order Ref: 19198	**Showtunes - Volume 1** Order Ref: 19103
Classic Hits - Volume 1 Order Ref: 19099	**Showtunes - Volume 2** Order Ref: 3328A
Classic Hits - Volume 2 Order Ref: 19100	**Soft Rock Collection** Order Ref: 4617A
Country Songs Order Ref: 19101	**Soul Classics** Order Ref: 19201
Traditional English Favourites Order Ref: 4229A	**Summer Collection** Order Ref: 3489A
Favourite Hymns Order Ref: 4179A	**TV Themes** Order Ref: 19196
Film Classics Order Ref: 19197	**The Twenties** Order Ref: 2969A
Great Songwriters Order Ref: 2225A	**The Thirties** Order Ref: 2970A
Instrumental Classics Order Ref: 2338A	**The Forties** Order Ref: 2971A
Traditional Irish Favourites Order Ref: 4230A	**The Fifties** Order Ref: 2972A
Love Songs - Volume 1 Order Ref: 19102	**The Sixties** Order Ref: 2973A
Love Songs - Volume 2 Order Ref: 19199	**The Seventies** Order Ref: 2974A
Music Hall Order Ref: 3329A	**The Eighties** Order Ref: 2975A
Motown Classics Order Ref: 2337A	**The Nineties** Order Ref: 2976A
Number One Hits Order Ref: 19200	**Wartime Collection** Order Ref: 3955A

Wedding Collection
Order Ref: 3688A

Exclusive distributors:

International Music Publications Limited
Griffin House 161 Hammersmith Road, London W6 8BS
International Music Publications Limited
25 Rue D'Hauteville, 75010 Paris, France
International Music Publications GmbH Germany
Marstallstrasse 8, D-80539 München, Germany
Nuova Carisch S.R.L.
Via M.F. Quintiliano 40, 20138 Milano, Italy
Danmusik
Vognmagergade 7, DK-1120 Copenhagen K, Denmark